The Old Lady of Wasilla Lake

A Story of the Red-necked Grebes
of Wasilla Lake, Alaska

by

Jack Randall

Illustrations by the Author

Cover images printed with permission:
Front artwork copyright Byron Birdsall.
Back photograph copyright Greg Downing Photography.
Author photograph ©2003 Clark James Mishler.

Text and inside illustrations copyright Jack Randall.

Published by Ulyssian Publications, an imprint of Pine Orchard, Inc.
Visit us on the internet at www.pineorchard.com.

Printed in Canada.

Printed using soy ink, also with recycled content,
including case fabric from Ecological Fibers, Inc.

ISBN 1-930580-81-9

EAN 978-1930580-81-7

Library of Congress Control Number 2005931108

Author's Notes

This account is derived from my personal observations over a period of fourteen seasons; daily journals for 2002, 2003, and 2004; and numerous photographs, some of which were taken from the shoreline — some fifty feet from the Old Lady's nest, others from my upstairs room which is one-hundred feet from her nest.

For more comprehensive data regarding the Red-necked Grebe, readers are directed to the references, compiled by Tamara Mills of the United States Fish and Wildlife Service.

This book is dedicated to the volunteers and professionals of the "Alaska Loon and Grebe Watch" who stand guard over the Grebes.

All profits from the sale of this book are hereby donated to support the "Grebe Watch" and to further research on behalf of the Red-necked Grebe and its habitat.

—Jack Randall
2005

Table of Contents

Acknowledgements

This work would not have been undertaken but for the care and kindness of my friend Tamara Mills (aka "The Grebe Girl"); her motivation brought it into being. Beyond his magnificent cover painting, Byron Birdsall inspired me to reach deep to find an unknown talent – to undertake the daunting task of illustration. With his exquisite photo image for the back cover, Greg Downing has completely embraced the "Old Lady" in fine art. My son-in-law, Jim Coe, has turned a neophyte's initial effort into a truly professional piece of work.

Don and Edna Chicarell brought their vast skills as educators to bear on the manuscript, and Edna subjected it to the scrutiny of eighty second grade students at Tanaina Elementary School. That these children were fully engaged by the "Old Lady" confirmed my intent that her story reach out to all age groups. My other young readers, McKenzie Pfister (age 10), Kira Baranowski (age 13), and Lindsey Miller (age 16) each made a valuable contribution to the book itself and thus to me personally.

One who was told by a third grade teacher that he had "no talent for art," yet at the age of seventy-five dares the illustration of his first book requires a lot of help. When, with not a little trepidation, I first ventured into Blaine's Art in Wasilla, I could not have conceived the depth of the response I received from Terri Pfister, Karen Whitworth, and my "teach" Gail Moses. Their professional help was invaluable; the continuing gifts of their time, support, and love extend beyond measure.

And finally, to my neighbors Danielle and Frazier Smith (dedicated grebe watchers in their own right), Keeley Porter (whose ministrations help keep both body and soul together), and my wife Mary (whose patience has been the underpinning of all else), I expected much from each; you, in turn, gave so much more.

Thank You All!

Introduction

The Red-necked Grebe (*Podiceps grisegena*) in Alaska breeds on small lakes and marshlands south of the Brooks Range, and winters in salt water from the Aleutian Islands through Southeast Alaska. Breeding pairs arrive at Wasilla Lake as soon as a strip of open water appears along the shoreline, generally from mid-April to mid-May when the long days of the sub-arctic summer begin. The courtship ritual commences shortly after arrival and frenetic nest building soon follows, the nest serving as both a mating and an incubation platform. The typical clutch of four to five eggs is laid over four to seven days with both male and female rotating the sitting chores for the twenty-five to thirty-day incubation period.

The newly hatched chicks are brooded under the wings of the sitting bird and are fed by the swimming bird that brings insects, leeches, and small fish.

Within two to three days, this "back-brooding" graduates to the water with the downy striped heads of the chicks peeking from between the wings of the "boat" bird. Although chicks are able to swim as soon as they are hatched, they frequently fall into the water and must scramble back onto the nest. Shared back-brooding continues for ten to fourteen days. After this point, rapid growth occurs and the chicks begin the three to four-month path to self-sufficiency.

Just before the ice begins to form in the fall, the now fully fledged juvenile grebes depart for the coast either with their parent adults or with other chicks of the year. Those who survive their first winter generally return to their "home lake," but these "immatures" only very rarely breed before their second year. They tend to congregate in open water, well away from nesting locations, and are clearly distinguishable by the white breast and neck versus the remarkable chestnut-red of the breeding adults, from which their name derives.

Preface

The heroine of this work, "The Old Lady of Wasilla Lake," first came under my scrutiny when my wife Mary and I moved to the north shore of Wasilla Lake, Alaska, in early June of 1991. We had, of course, seen the Red-necked Grebe sitting on her nest just offshore and heard the raucous chatter between her and her mate as he gathered sticks and submerged grasses to reinforce their floating home; but it wasn't until a knowledgeable and observant landscape worker called attention to the deformity on the female's upper mandible (bill) that we took notice and the saga that follows gradually began to emerge.

This tale of avian tenacity in the face of seemingly overwhelming odds is addressed to two distinct levels of comprehension: the first to teens and adults that they may better understand how closely life in the natural world is mirrored in our own; and secondly, to younger children that they may mature with a broader appreciation of the creatures with whom they share their environment. It is told in the "words" of the heroic grebe. The illustrations, taken together with their textual references, tell of the grebes' experiences at the level of younger children.

Beginnings
1989

My ancestors first came to Wasilla Lake not long after the last glaciers receded, perhaps some ten-thousand years ago. I was hatched in mid-June of 1989 on a floating island nest that my parents had built over a month previously. My egg tooth broke the shell and almost as soon as I had unfolded my damp downy being, my mother kicked me out of the nest and into the icy water! Instinctively, but with great fear, I swam back to the nest, scrambled on and crawled under the sheltering wings of my mother. I felt and looked more like a turtle than a bird!

Another surprise: I had a brother! In the warm safe darkness, we huddled together — a togetherness we would share for the next month — even as we constantly competed for food and the attention of our parents. A grebe's life is not an easy one and from the very beginning, our parents prepared us for the rigors ahead. They shared the duties of maintaining the nest and bringing crustaceans, insects, leeches, and small fish for us to eat and to fight over!

To protect our sensitive young stomachs, our first food consisted of soft downy feathers offered by our parents. We soon learned to sense the approach of the swimming bird and up popped our heads from between the wings of the sitting bird, our little necks stretching to be the first to be fed.

Sometimes, when our sitting parent needed a break to feed, instead of food, we would be subjected to the dreaded "chick-drop." Our shelter would suddenly rise, lift its wings, and we would tumble out helter-skelter onto the nest and into the water!

On other less traumatic occasions, our shelter would launch itself gently from the nest and become a "boat" upon which we proudly rode with little heads and necks protruding from between folded wings. Thus, we gradually became accustomed to the water where we would spend all of our lives; for after all, we were aquatic birds!

After three weeks of "back-brooding" the nest was no longer necessary and we left it to the ravages of wind and wave. We ranged further and further about the lake yet always returned to our "home" location; marking it well in memory, for this special place would play a crucial role in a future we could not yet comprehend.

My brother and I passed two critical survival points; at ten and thirty days of life. No marauding muskrat or magpie had stolen us as an egg; no loon or otter or mink had killed us while we were tiny and unable to escape; and no seagull or eagle had snatched us from the water's surface before we were wise enough and strong enough to dive into the depths for protection. Now it was time to eat and grow strong.

The Cottonwood Creek drainage, of which Wasilla Lake is a part, supports a substantial run of Salmon, the young of which are present in the lake at the time of maximum growth for us grebes. On their migration to the sea, these four to six-inch smolts form the mainstay of our diet. As I grew larger, my extended neck would even accommodate a Rainbow Trout of some ten inches in length — a filling meal indeed! Soon I began to dive deeper and longer, and found I could partly feed myself. The water warmed and there were many Caddis Fly larvae and as their nymph stage rose toward the surface I could easily catch them; when they emerged as adult Caddis Flies, I went crazy with ecstasy!

ADULT CADDIS FLY

ADAMS ARTIFICIAL FLY

With growth and strength in my wings and large lobed feet, I discovered I could almost fly under water and as soon as my bill grew long enough, I began to catch small fish on my own. The Sticklebacks' spines made me thankful for those early feathers! As a female, I paired with my mother and together we explored more and more of the lake.

Mine was not the only family of grebes on Wasilla Lake, but we kept our distance from the others; we were not very sociable.

Immature birds who ventured too close were quickly driven off by screaming and with charges both on the surface and under the water as well. Once I even saw my mother fly through the air and I thought, "There sure is an awful lot to learn about being a grebe."

Boats were my most frightening discovery! Low in the water and small in size, even an adult grebe cannot see very far because of the curvature of the earth, so we must stretch our necks to see anything more than

a few yards away. Imagine if what you heard and saw was a huge monster bearing down upon you at tremendous speed; only a panic dive would take you away from certain destruction! On some days, they were everywhere! Nonetheless, our parents ventured out amongst them to teach us how to escape. While the boats were out, I preferred to stay close to shore where my nest had been. Only at night or when the winds and waves came, did I wish to go out upon the far reaches of the lake.

In August, longer nights returned to the lake and the peaceful hours rapidly increased. My flight feathers were growing and I had an urge to fly, but my brother was not having much success. A grebe must "taxi" for takeoff by running across the water with wings flapping frantically. My father, with his new strong primary quills to replace those he had recently lost, could once again get airborne. My brother crashed each time he tried!

My mother said we must wait as she was still too weak and besides, we had plenty of time. Grebes rarely fly during the breeding, brooding, nurturing season, and then just for short distances at very low levels. Only when migrating, do we fly long distances and then almost exclusively at night.

September brought strong storms and the immatures from last year left Wasilla Lake for their wintering waters on the coast.

One or two chicks that had hatched very early went with them. Now, using the wind for lift, my flying lessons began: paddle, run, flap, and splash. I wanted to stay on the lake and eat fish; but in October, snow began to fall and the lake began to freeze. So when the wind was right, the family took off together one moonlit night, flying south toward Kachemak Bay and salt water. Here we floated so high in the water we could get airborne with much greater ease, but we had to work harder to catch the new fish we had found.

Once again, we waited for a favorable wind and flew to a protected cove on East Amatuli Island, one of the Barren Islands. They are about halfway between the Kenai Peninsula and Afognak Island, and lie within the Gulf of Alaska Unit of the Alaska Maritime Wildlife Refuge. There was even a navigation light to welcome us!

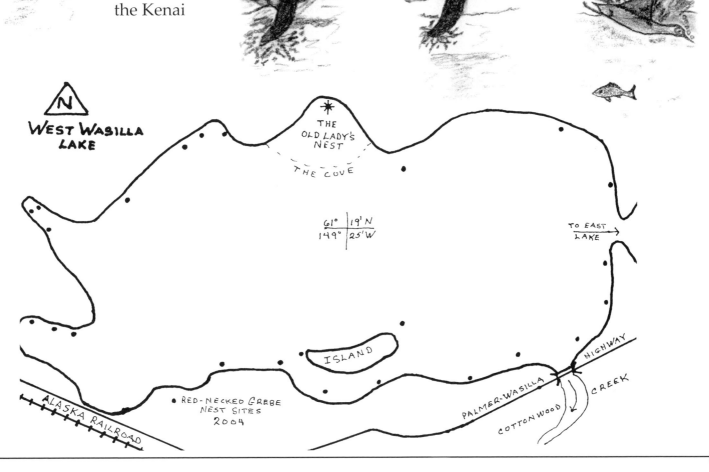

WEST WASILLA LAKE

N

THE OLD LADY'S NEST

THE COVE

61° | 19' N
149° | 25' W

TO EAST LAKE

ISLAND

HIGHWAY

PALMER-WASILLA

COTTONWOOD CREEK

ALASKA RAILROAD

• RED-NECKED GREBE NEST SITES 2004

Here, we found grebes from Wasilla Lake and many other places. There were also new birds: Puffins, Murres, Cormorants, and Guillemots. There were new dangers from Sea Lions and Killer Whales; from powerful williwaw winds that blew straight down from the high peak above the cove; and huge waves that crashed upon the rocks at the entrance to our refuge. Yet, seeming to spite the hostile local conditions, the warm waters of the Japan Current brought us a great abundance of fish and here I would spend many winters.

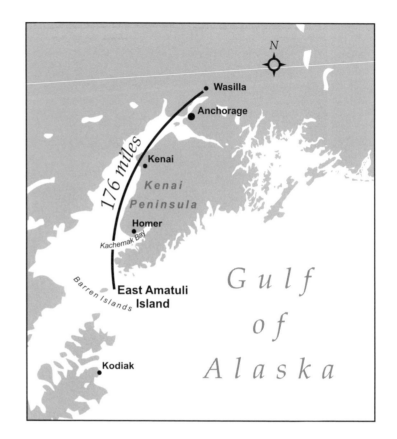

EAST AMATULI ISLAND
Lat 58° 55" North   Long 159° 00" West

CORMORANTS

PUFFINS

PUFFIN PEAK
1539 FEET

REFUGE COVE

LIGHT

KILLER WHALES

S

SEA LIONS

Transition
1990

In the spring, the mature grebes, my mother and father among them, left early for their flights to their home-nesting waters. On Wasilla Lake, they arrived on the very day a little bit of the shore ice thawed and left a small channel of open water. We immatures — the hatchlings from the prior year — didn't yet really know what we were supposed to do, only somehow sensing it was time to go "home." When we arrived, the adults were making strange noises and doing strange dances; when we went to see what all the excitement was about, we were told in no uncertain terms to get lost! After that rude treatment, like most early adolescents, we flocked together in the middle of the lake and kept our distance — never again daring to go near even our "own" nest or the chicks when they hatched. We spent the summer fishing and swimming and gradually growing up. The girls flirted with the boys; the boys chased the girls; and the girls swam away, laughing "krick — kree, hee, hee, hee!"

When a young male grebe fell prey to an eagle, one very precocious member of our flock flew to the side of the stricken female. The plumage of his neck soon reddened and together they built a nest and raised a chick right next door to my home nest. Mating at such an early age occurs only very infrequently.

In early October, we left the lake and once again flew to East Amatuli Island. By the following spring, we had undergone many mysterious changes — we had become adults.

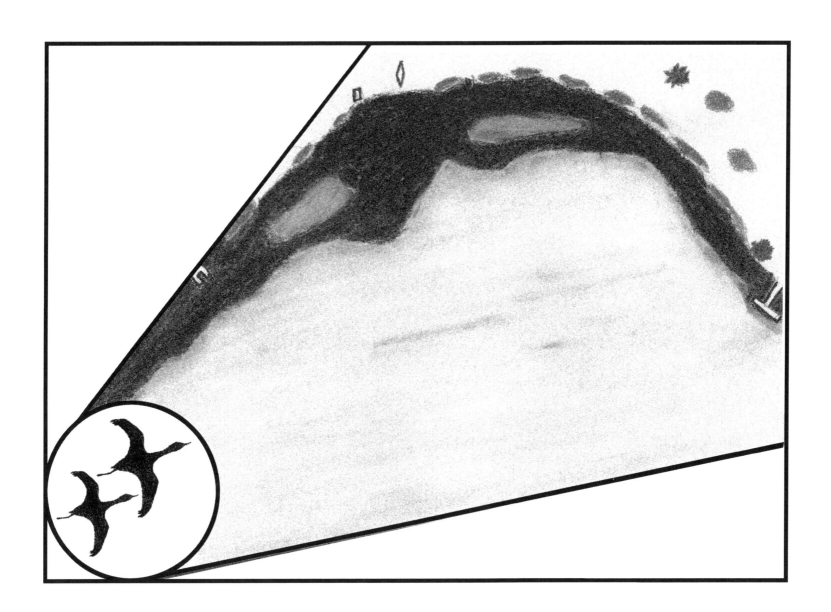

The Cycle of Life Continues
1991

Neither my mother nor my father survived the winter. In early April while my chest and neck were still in their white winter plumage, a handsome young male, already with a neck of reddish chestnut, swam up and offered me some eel grass. I didn't take it, so he left and soon returned with a fish. I couldn't resist. When I accepted it, he told me that he found the triangular bump on the right side of my upper mandible absolutely irresistible! I, of course, had seen this anomaly; but now, I felt very special and somehow sensed that

I was destined to be mated to this male and that we would share much joy and could endure much hardship. As we faced the future, the fact that we would share it together would sustain us. Our union was for life.

In mid-April, on the back of a strong southwest wind, we flew straight to Wasilla Lake. I knew that, although most of the lake was still frozen, there was open water near the site of my home nest and to this very spot I led my mate. As soon as we landed, we touched bills in a posture that resembled the shape of a harp, and then flared our crests as we swam rapidly side by side — "rushing" — and for the first time making the "whinney-bray" mating call of the Red-necked Grebe. The days grew longer and warmer — it was a magical time. The last of the ice melted and mating calls echoed day and night as the urge to reproduce rose to a crescendo!

The nest of the Red-necked Grebe serves as both a mating platform and a haven upon which to lay and incubate the eggs. My natal nest was in a shallow cove, bordered by overhanging willows and alders whose fallen dead branches formed the structural base of the nest. Abundant grasses and reeds with which to bind our new nest in some places grew to the surface. I gave my mate instructions as to what was needed next, and he hurried off to find it.

Given a solid foundation, a pair of grebes can build a nest overnight!

We grebes are excellent engineers, but it takes time to hone the skills required to construct a durable nest. In the beginning, both male and female gather materials and weave them together until the nest will support her. At this point, the male becomes the dominant gatherer and the female the primary builder.

Alas, in our hurry and inexperience, we had selected a deep water site and thus failed to attach the nest securely to the grass on the lake bottom. Before I could conceive and lay an egg, wind-driven waves tore our nest to shreds! We frantically rebuilt — on the same, dumb spot — and this time, I produced a clutch of three eggs, only once again, after two weeks, to lose all to the pounding of the waves!

With cooled ardor, we gradually settled down to resting posture: head, neck, and bill tucked in so we resembled small round ornaments as we floated on the glassy surface of the lake. We kept close to home and close to each other; on occasion, we would touch bills, bray softly, and venture forth to feed. The color of our plumage faded with our passion and in September, with no chicks to nurture and train, we flew back to East Amatuli Island.

The Long Years

1992 – 2001

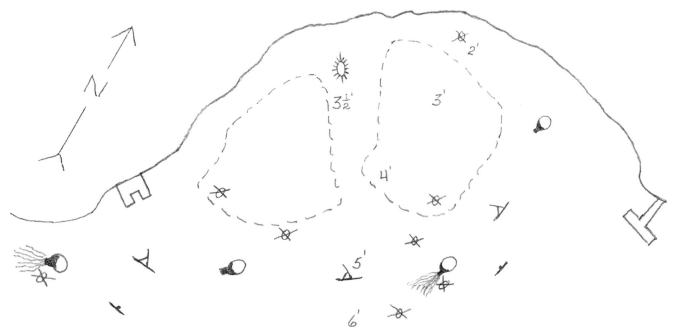

N

X 2'

☼ 3½'

3'

4'

5'

6'

THE SANCTUARY
IN THE
COVE

FEATURES

☼ NEST 1999-2004

X UNSUCCESSFUL NESTS

〰 GRASS ATTACHED
TO BUOY

◯ ORANGE BUOY

△ FLOATING SIGN

⊥ FIXED SIGN
ON POLE

SCALE ½" = 50'

[⌐ ⌐] AREA OF WAVE
BLOCKING WEEDS

⊥L DOCK

NOTE: FEATURES NOT TO
SCALE FOR CLARITY

Location – location - location!!! As with any residential property, its value depends primarily on its location. This was especially true for my nest in the cove on Wasilla Lake. Build too far from shore and, as in our first nest, the water is too deep. In addition, the waves are larger and the nest is too tempting a target for unobservant or inconsiderate boaters. Build too close to shore, and incubating eggs are certain prey for mink and muskrats, even house cats!

With a shallow water nest, its supporting column is too short to insulate against heavy wave action and can be pulled under by a sudden rise in the water level.

In 1995, after a heartless jet-ski driver had deliberately destroyed our nest and its five eggs, the people onshore posted signs warning boats to "Steer Clear" and later, they added buoys to mark the line beyond which motor boats should not venture.

Over time, we came to sense that a sanctuary had been created for us. So we attached our nest to a buoy. Five times we did this; but, of course, when the wind rose, the buoy slapped the nest to smithereens.

As the years rolled by, the disasters mounted. A colony of muskrats came to the shore of the cove and sure enough stole every egg I laid in 1997 – eleven in all!

Red-necked Grebes are ancient at eight years of age and 1997 was my eighth. Once again, my mate and I flew to East Amatuli Island, determined to try again in the spring. In 1998, we saw one storm after another and try as we might, no nest survived.

Upon our return in 1999, the water level in Wasilla Lake had begun to drop and we noticed a small area where the largest waves, regardless of the wind direction,

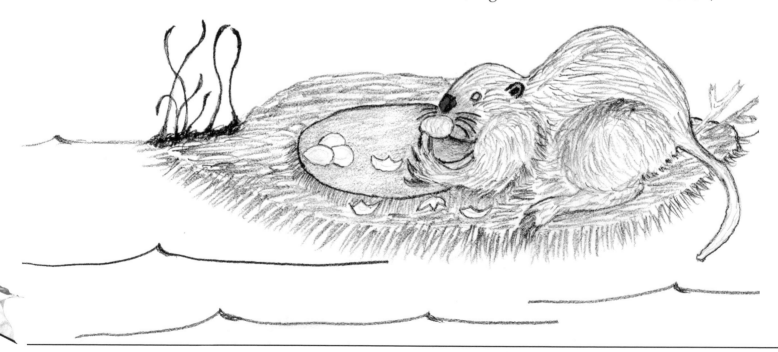

were so attenuated as to cause no problem for our nest! This was due to the lower water level and the consequent heavy weed growth that formed a natural breakwater. To add to our apparent good fortune, the depth of the water was now ideal and strong grass grew right in the center of this "oasis." With renewed vigor, we set about building our dream nest. Conditions were perfect. Our union produced five fine eggs. For thirty-five days, we incubated them. None hatched. One by one, I cast them from the nest. There was no life in them.

When we returned from our winter waters in the spring of 2000, we found the foundation of our previous nest still intact. But once more, no chicks were hatched. With the same result in 2001, I thought that "irresistible bump" of mine to be a curse! Perhaps I was sterile! Eleven years of trying and not a single chick had seen the light of day. For what I was certain would be the last time, we flew laboriously back to East Amatuli Island. Shortly after landing in our refuge cove, my mate dove beneath the waves, never to be seen again.

The Legacy

2002

The life force is very strong and somehow I made it through to my fourteenth spring! Of a sudden, from out of the sea-mist, a handsome young male once again approached and offered me some eel grass. Was this déjà vu? Was I dreaming? This time, I did not wait for a fish! There would be another chance!

Spring came very late to Wasilla Lake in 2002. Yet, with knowledge born of eons of grebe history, my young lothario and I landed in the cove on the fourth of June; the last pans of rotting ice had just broken up. For two idyllic weeks, we repeated the courting rituals — over and over again! By the fifteenth, our nest, built

on the foundation from the three previous years, emerged stronger than ever and by the eighteenth, the first egg was laid. I stood tall on the edge of the nest and shivered and shuddered with joy!

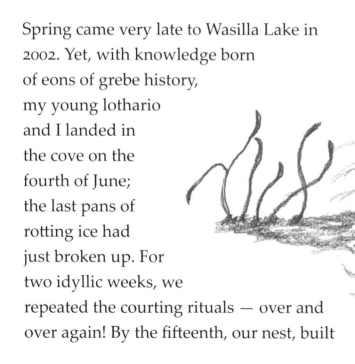

I laid three eggs in all and was content to handle most of the incubation, too tired to do very much active feeding. By contrast, my hyperactive young mate was everywhere! He provided me with leeches and fish as though I were a newly hatched chick, practicing for what surely was to be his first stint as a parent. Under my tutelage, he scurried back and forth, bringing more grass and sticks to reinforce the nest – it was indeed a mighty fortress!

At the same time, the muskrats at the shore were also den building. Their numbers were astounding, their wakes striping the surface of the cove from headland to headland! The big "bull" muskrat looked

more like a beaver! But when he ventured too near the nest, my mate raced to deny him his intended egg dinner. When, on July seventeenth, the first chick hatched, my champion attacked those devilish rodents with such vengeance that the gray fur flew far and wide!

The second chick was hatched on July nineteenth. Two miracles had issued forth from the union of my aged body, now six years beyond the known life expectancy of a Red-necked Grebe and that of my precious, precocious protector. Now, the task of rearing our legacy began in earnest.

From the earliest brooding on the nest and the back-brooding on the water, the second chick to hatch (a male) was dominant. The other (a female) was quiescent; last to get food, last to swim, last to dive, and even then not far from the nest or my side. We girls were a perfect pair. The adventures of the boys, on the other hand, were a sight and a fright to behold!

One day, four juvenile Pacific Loons landed on the lake and immediately swam toward the nest. I was very anxious. When the loons were about fifty feet away the lead loon and my mate stood very tall on the water and hunched their spread wings in intimidation. My mate dove beneath the surface and with synchronous kicks of his large webbed feet and powerful thrusts from his wings, he emerged from the water like a missile,

struck the loon's exposed breast, knocking him over backwards and drawing copious amounts of blood! The loons fled the lake and never returned. My fearless mate deserves the grebe "medal of honor"!

By mid-August, my mate and our now juvenile male offspring were ranging far into the lake. Junior was diving for his own fish and had begun flight training. Over and over again, he would try to emulate his father; time and time again, he would crash and splash. It took him two weeks to finally earn his wings! Now, whenever a threat arose, the two would appear from out of nowhere to defend the nest site. By mid-September, the female began to fly, but still required help in catching the larger fish she needed to build enough strength to fly to East Amatuli Island. Whenever my mate would approach with a fish for her, she would rush to meet him with wings rapidly slapping the water — this behavior I called "Happy Flapping." I also found it useful for cooling down in very hot weather.

The nighttime hours grew longer, the winds grew stronger, and the temperature often fell below freezing, signaling that it would soon be time to leave. The immatures were the first to go, accompanied by the more precocious juveniles. For us, it was not yet time.

We made some longer range forays, but eventually the four of us always returned to the nest site within the sanctuary. My mate seemed to sense a special commission to train our young and to protect and provide until the last possible moment.

And then one evening in October, we two females were left all alone in the cove. Or at least so we thought until a ghostly apparition appeared in the form of a much larger grebe! He was so sleek and oh so suave! His head, neck, and chest were snowy white with a coal black cap extending down the back half of his neck, spreading out to join his wings folded alongside his inky back.

This "Ghost Grebe" made a few dives, rose tall upon the water with wings outstretched, and then swam off into the mist that had begun to rise from the chilling surface.

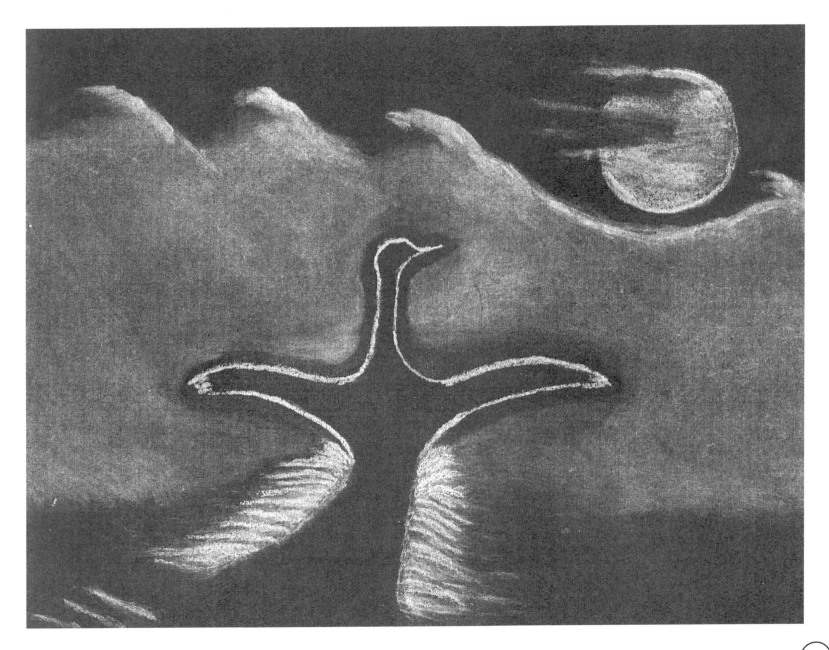

It was time: time to begin the final journey.

Epilogue

November 28, 2002

Wasilla Lake froze soon after the "Old Lady" left, only to thaw in a spell of unseasonably warm weather. The "Ghost Grebe" reappeared at the nesting site, swam a few circles, and took off, flying toward the East. It was Thanksgiving Day, and the author of this book gave thanks for the company of the grebes and for the privilege of witnessing the miracle of "The Old Lady of Wasilla Lake."

2003

The "Old Lady" never returned; however, her ambitious young mate arrived at the cove with a new much younger female. Soon after, an immature (the "Happy Flapper"?) swam in and began circling as though familiar with the place; she was nearly dispatched for her untimely intrusion!

As soon as the revitalized nest began to emerge, that old nemesis, the oversize muskrat, showed up to inspect. He was last seen rounding the eastern point of the cove with fur flying into the air from the incessant pecking of the dauntless young male. There have since been no muskrat sightings in the vicinity!

Four chicks were hatched in 2003 from a total of nine eggs laid by the prolific new pair! Two were brooded by each partner and all survived to fly out in the fall.

2004

It took an unknown disaster and a subsequent second clutch of four eggs to produce three chicks in 2004. Within a week, the first born disappeared. Having passed the critical thirty-day survival period, the remaining two, now fledged, appear to be well on their way toward contributing to the legacy of "The Old Lady of Wasilla Lake."

Addendum

Rarely reported so far from its normal range in British Columbia and Northern Alberta, the "Ghost Grebe" of this story was identified as a Western Grebe (*Aechmophorus occidentalis*).

A careful count of the western half of Wasilla Lake in August of 2004 revealed a total of 115 Red-necked Grebes:

44 Adults   40 Chicks   31 Immatures

A preliminary count in early May of 2005 indicated a total of 53 Red-necked Grebes:

24 Pair and 5 Singles — no Immatures

References
(Compiled by Tamara K. Mills, USFWS)

Bucher, C. 1997. Rabbitkettle lake indicator species monitoring program, Nahanni National Park Reserve. Unpublished data report 96-3/NAH: 1-31.

Cringan, A.T. 1957. Notes on the biology of the Red-necked grebe in Western Ontario. Canadian Field-Naturalist 71: 72-73.

Davis, E.J. 1983. Red-necked Grebe making nest-building movements in winter. Breeding Birds 76(3): 135.

De Smet, K.D. 1982. Status report on: the Red-necked Grebe (Podiceps Grisegena) in Canada. Committee on the Status of Endangered Wildlife in Canada, Ottawa, Ontario.

De Smet, K.D. 1983. Breeding ecology and productivity of Red-necked Grebes in Turtle Mountain Provincial Park, Manitoba. M.S. thesis, University of North Dakota, Grand Forks.

De Smet, K.D. 1987. Organochlorines, predators and reproductive success of the Red-necked Grebe in southern Manitoba. Condor 89: 460-467.

Fournier, M.A., and J.E. Hines. 1998. Breeding ecology and status of the Red-necked Grebe, Podiceps grisegena, in the subarctic of the Northwest Territories. Can. Field-Nat. 112: (in press).

Forsyth, D.J., P.A. Martin, K.D. De Smet, and M.E. Riske. 1994. Organochlorine contaminants and eggshell thinning in grebes from prairie Canada. Environmental Pollution 85:51-58.

Garner, L.A. 1991. Intra- and interspecific aggression by Red-necked Grebes. M.S. thesis, North Dakota State University, Fargo.

Gunn, W.W.H. 1951. The changing status of the Red-necked Grebe in Southern Ontario. Can. Field-Nat. 65: 143-145.

Heglund, P.J. 1988. Relations between waterbird use and the limnological characteristics of wetlands on Yukon Flats National Wildlife Refuge, Alaska. M.S. thesis. Univ. of Missouri, Columbia.

Keller, V. 1989. Variations in the response of Great Crested Grebes Podiceps cristatus to Human Disturbance-a sign of adaptation? Biological Conservation 49: 31-45.

Kevan, C.L. 1970. An ecological study of Red-necked Grebes on Astotin Lake Alberta. M.S. thesis, University of Alberta, Edmonton.

McAllister, N.M. 1963. Ontogeny of behaviour in five species of grebes. Ph.D. diss., Univ. of British Columbia, Vancouver.

Mills, T. K. 2004. The effects of human disturbance on common loon and Red-necked grebe breeding success in southcentral Alaska. M.S. thesis, University of Alaska Anchorage.

Munro, J.A. 1941. The grebes: studies of waterfowl in British Columbia. British Columbia Prov. Mus. Occ. Pap. No. 3.

Ohanjanian, I.A. 1986. Effects of a man-made dyke on the reproductive behavior and nesting success of Red-necked Grebes. M.S. thesis, Simon Fraser University, Burnaby, BC.

Ohanjanian, I.A. 1989. Food flights of Red-necked Grebes during the breeding season. J. Field Ornithol. 60: 143-153.

Randall, J. 2003. In the company of grebes: A 12 year odyssey. Unpublished Report. Wasilla, Alaska, USA.

Riske, M.E. Environmental and human impacts upon grebes breeding in Central Alberta. Ph.D. diss., Univ. of Calgary, Alberta.

Simmons, K.E.L. 1970. Duration of dives in the Red-necked Grebe. Breeding Birds 63: 300-302.

Storer, R.W. and G.L. Nuechterlein. 1992. Western and Clark's Grebe. In The Birds of North America, No. 26 (A. Poole, P. Steetenheim, and F. Gill, Eds). Philadelphia: The Academy of Natural Sciences; Washington, DC: The American Ornithologists Union.

Stout, B.E. 1995. Fall migration of Red-necked Grebes in the Great Lakes Region. M.S. Thesis, North Dakota State University, Fargo.

Stout, B. E., and G. L. Nuechterlein. 1999. Red-necked Grebe (Podiceps Grisegena). In The Birds of North America, Number 465, A. Poole and F. Gill, Eds). The Birds of North America, Inc., Philadelphia, PA.

U.S. Fish and Wildlife Service. 1984. Habitat suitability index models: Western Grebe. U.S. Fish Wildl. Serv. FWS/OBS-82/10.69.

Author's Note

Since one goal of this book is to establish the Red-necked Grebe as an "Indicator Species" for determination of watershed quality, the segment on Caddis Flies is not accidental. The interrelationship between indicator insects and other inhabitants of the Cottonwood Creek drainage (i.e., trout, salmon, loons, grebes, humans, etc.) will become of ever greater importance in guiding land use decisions and the need for habitat protection. Interested parties are directed to the websites of the Tree of Life and the U.S. Environmental Protection Agency.

Thank You for Supporting
The Alaska Loon and Grebe Watch

The Alaska Loon and Grebe Watch is a volunteer-based monitoring project under the direction of the Alaska Citizen Science Program — a partnership of the United States Fish and Wildlife Service, Migratory Bird Management Office; the Alaska Department of Fish and Game; Chugach National Forest; The Alaska Zoo; and the Alaska Natural Heritage Program.

Some of the present and future projects of this program include:

+ Expanding the twenty-year-old Alaska Loon Watch by recruiting and training an additional cadre of volunteers.

+ Implantation of satellite transmitters in Red-necked Grebes to more closely define their migratory patterns and wintering territories.

+ To establish additional web-cam sites for monitoring the behavior of both species.

The net proceeds from the sale of this book will be deposited into an account established with The Alaska Community Foundation for the benefit of The Alaska Loon & Grebe Watch. Kindly fill out the form on this page; a receipt indicating the tax-deductible portion of the cover price will be mailed to you after the close of the year of purchase.

Additional fully tax-deductible contributions are always most welcome. *Please make checks payable to:* ALASKA COMMUNITY FOUNDATION *for the benefit of:* THE ALASKA LOON & GREBE WATCH FUND *and mail to:*

THE ALASKA COMMUNITY FOUNDATION
701 WEST 8TH AVENUE SUITE 230
ANCHORAGE, ALASKA 99501

NAME* _____

EMAIL ADDRESS** _____

MAILING ADDRESS* _____

CITY* _____

STATE* _____ ZIP CODE* _____

*REQUIRED   **OPTIONAL

For further information:

Tamara K. Mills
USFWS, Alaska Loon & Grebe Watch
1 (907) 786–3517

Marcia Hastings
Director Alaska Community Foundation
1 (907) 265-6044